Andrew Brodie Basics
LET'S DO MENTAL MATHS

FOR AGES 7-8

with over **100** reward stickers

- Over 800 practice questions
- Regular progress tests
- Extra tips and brain booster questions

First published 2013 by Bloomsbury Publishing plc
50 Bedford Square, London, WC1B 3DP
www.bloomsbury.com

ISBN 978-1-4081-8336-6

Copyright © 2013 Bloomsbury Publishing plc
Written by Andrew Brodie
Design by Marcus Duck
Cover and inside illustrations of Digit the Dog and Andrew Brodie © Nikalas Catlow

10 9 8 7 6 5 4

A CIP record for this publication is available from the British Library.

Printed in China by Leo Paper Products

This book is produced using paper that is made from wood grown in managed, sustainable forests. It is natural, renewable and recyclable. The logging and manufacturing processes conform to the environmental regulations of the country of origin.

To see our full range of titles visit www.bloomsbury.com

BLOOMSBURY

Notes for parents

What's in this book

This is the third book in an exciting new series of *Andrew Brodie Basics: Let's Do Mental Maths* books. Each book contains more than 800 mental maths questions specially devised to boost children's confidence by providing plenty of practice in all the key aspects of the National Curriculum:

- Number and place value
- Addition and subtraction
- Multiplication and division
- Fractions
- Measures
- Geometry

The structure of each test follows the same pattern but the questions become gradually more difficult as the book progresses. You will notice that some questions are repeated to help your child learn and then revise vital facts such as identifying shapes: squares, triangles, rectangles and circles. Taking the time to discuss the questions with your child and helping to explain anything they find difficult will produce the best results. Answers to all the questions are provided at the back of the book.

How you can help

To begin with your child might find the tests quite tricky but as they work their way through the book and become more familiar with the different types of question their confidence will grow. At the end of every five tests there is a Progress Test which will help you and your child to review some of the key concepts and will also highlight anything they haven't understood so far. Always provide lots of encouragement and explain that they should learn from their mistakes rather than be disheartened.

Children gain confidence by learning facts that they can use in their work at school. Help your child by displaying posters on their bedroom wall, showing facts such as the times tables, days of the week and months of the year. Talk about these facts with your child and other topics that children find difficult such as fractions.

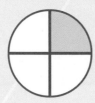

Explain that the circle is cut into four pieces so we are dealing with quarters; 1 of these is shaded so the fraction shaded is one quarter. We write one quarter like this:

$$\frac{1}{4}$$

Some children have difficulty with the concept of a fraction of a set of objects.

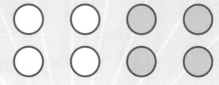

The fraction shown here is, of course, $\frac{4}{8}$ and some children will quickly see that this is the same as $\frac{1}{2}$. Other children simply won't get it! If this is the case it's best to encourage them to identify the fraction correctly as $\frac{4}{8}$ and return to discussing it later, perhaps as long as 6 months or even a year later. Concepts that proved tricky to begin with can suddenly fall into place. It's most important that children don't feel pressurized into tackling questions that are beyond their conceptual understanding. With patience, praise and encouragement they will grasp concepts at an appropriate stage in their development and are likely then to gallop ahead.

Digit the Dog and Brain Boosters

Look out for useful tips from Digit the Dog who provides little snippets of mathematical information that your child needs to know or quick questions to get them thinking!

Brodie's Brain Boosters feature short mathematical problems, which can be solved by working logically. Some of these may look very straightforward but the thinking processes that your child will need to apply are important skills to practise, ready for more challenging work later. Understanding the wording of questions is a crucial aspect of problem solving so ensure that your child reads each question carefully – give some help with the vocabulary if necessary.

With lots of practice and encouragement your child will see their score improve day by day!

TEST 1

Score:

1. What number is 10 more than 27?

2. 9 + 8 =

3. 19 minus 5 =

4. 79 – 6 =

5. 9 x 2 =

6. 2 multiplied by 7 =

7. Share 8 between 2.

8. 20 ÷ 2 =

9. Count in tens: 0, 10, 20, 30…
   What number comes next?

10. Write these numbers in order
    (smallest first): 87 78 97

11. What fraction is shaded?

12. Colour one tenth of the circle.

13. What time does the clock show?

14. How many seconds are there in one minute?

15. 1 metre =   centimetres

16. How many grams are there in one kilogram?

17. How much money altogether?

18. How much liquid in the cylinder?

19. What shape is this?

20. What number does the tally show?

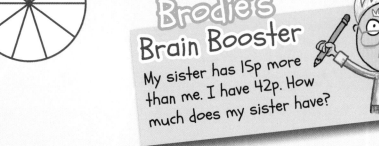

Brodie's Brain Booster

My sister has 15p more than me. I have 42p. How much does my sister have?

TEST 2

1 What number is 10 more than 48?

2 7 + 6 =

3 22 minus 6 =

4 85 – 4 =

5 6 x 2 =

6 2 multiplied by 8 =

7 Share 20 between 2.

8 12 ÷ 2 =

9 Count in tens: 30, 40, 50, 60…
What number comes next?

10 Write these numbers in order
(smallest first): 43 23 32

11 What fraction
is shaded?

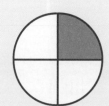

12 Colour two
tenths of
the circle.

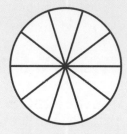

13 What time does the
clock show?

14 1 minute = seconds

15 How many centimetres are
there in one metre?

16 1 kilogram = grams

17 How much
money altogether?

18 How much liquid
in the cylinder?

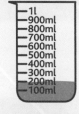

19 What shape is this?

20 What number does the tally show?

Digit says…

My tail is half a
metre long. That's 50
whole centimetres!

4

TEST 3

Score:

1 What number is 10 more than 61?

2 5 + 9 =

3 31 minus 4 =

4 93 − 7 =

5 8 x 2 =

6 2 multiplied by 7 =

7 Share 18 between 2.

8 24 ÷ 2 =

9 Count in tens: 20, 30, 40, 50…
What number comes next?

10 Write these numbers in order
(smallest first): 65 56 59

11 What fraction
is shaded?

12 Colour three
tenths of
the circle.

13 What time does the
clock show?

14 1 hour =   minutes

15 ½ metre =   centimetres

16   kilogram = 1000grams

17 How much
money altogether?

18 How much liquid
in the cylinder?

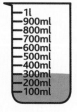

19 What shape is this?

20 What number does the tally show?

Brodie's Brain Booster

My sister has 5 fewer stamps than me. I have 62 stamps. How many does my sister have?

5

TEST 4

1 What number is 10 more than 93?

2 8 + 4 =

3 17 minus 8 =

4 54 – 6 =

5 4 x 2 =

6 2 multiplied by 5 =

7 Share 16 between 2.

8 14 ÷ 2 =

9 Count in tens: 50, 60, 70, 80…
What number comes next?

10 Write these numbers in order
(smallest first): 52 35 25

11 What fraction
is shaded?

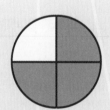

12 Colour four
tenths of
the circle.

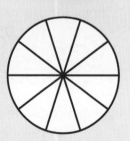

13 What time does the
clock show?

14 ½ hour =   minutes

15 100 centimetres =   metre

16 How many grams are
there in half a kilogram?

17 How much
money altogether?

18 How much liquid
in the cylinder?

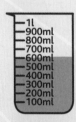

19 What shape is this?

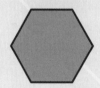

20 What number does the tally show?

TEST 5

Score:

1 What number is 10 more than 36?

2 9 + 6 =

3 18 minus 5 =

4 62 – 8 =

5 7 x 2 =

6 2 multiplied by 4 =

7 Share 14 between 2.

8 24 ÷ 2 =

9 Count in tens: 40, 50, 60, 70…
What number comes next?

10 Write these numbers in order
(smallest first): 71 17 77

11 What fraction
is shaded?

12 Colour five
tenths of
the circle.

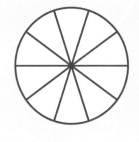

13 What time does the
clock show?

14 How many minutes are there
in one hour?

15 50cm =   metre

16 $\frac{1}{2}$ kilogram =   grams

17 How much
money altogether?

18 How much liquid
in the cylinder?

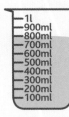

19 What shape is this?

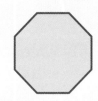

20 What number does the tally show?

Brodie's
Brain Booster

Four children each have 3
pairs of shoes. How many
shoes do they have altogether?

7

Addition

1 What number is 10 more than 85?

2 5 + 8 =

Subtraction

3 17 minus 6 =

4 89 – 8 =

Multiplication

5 11 x 2 =

6 2 multiplied by 8 =

Division

7 Share 24 between 2.

8 18 ÷ 2 =

Number and place value

9 Count in tens: 60, 70, 80, 90...
What number comes next?

10 Write these numbers in order,
smallest first. 92 99 29

Fractions

11 What fraction
is shaded?

12 Colour six tenths
of the circle.

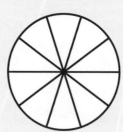

Measures

13 What time does
the clock show?

14 How many minutes are there in
half an hour?

15 1m =   cm

16   kg = 500g

17 How much
money altogether?

16 How much liquid
in the cylinder?

Geometry

19 What shape is this?

Data

20 What number does the tally show?

Score chart

Test	1	2	3	4	5	Progress
Score						

Score:

1 What is the sum of 9 and 8?

2 50 + 30 =

3 What number is 10 less than 84?

4 130 – 80 =

5 6 x 5 =

6 5 multiplied by 9 =

7 Divide 40 by 5.

8 25 ÷ 5 =

9 Count in hundreds: 0, 100, 200, 300… What number comes next?

10 Write these numbers in order (smallest first): 46 164 146

11 What fraction is shaded?

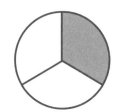

12 Colour seven tenths of the circle.

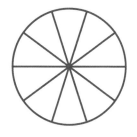

13 What time does the clock show?

14 How many hours are there in one day?

15 1 metre =   centimetres

16 How many grams are there in two kilograms?

17 How much money altogether?

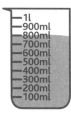

18 How much liquid in the cylinder?

19 What shape is this?

20 What number does the tally show?

|||| |||| ||||

9

TEST 7

Score:

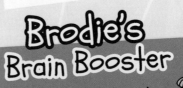

Four children each have 10 pairs of socks. How many socks do they have altogether?

1 What is the sum of 7 and 4?

2 60 + 20 =

3 What number is 10 less than 93?

4 180 – 50 =

5 3 x 5 =

6 5 multiplied by 6 =

7 Divide 20 by 5.

8 35 ÷ 5 =

9 Count in hundreds: 100, 200, 300, 400… What number comes next?

10 Write these numbers in order (smallest first): 312 32 132

11 What fraction is shaded?

12 Colour eight tenths of the circle.

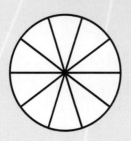

13 What time does the clock show?

14 1 day =   hours

15 2 metres =   centimetres

16 2000g =   kg

17 How much money altogether?

18 How much liquid in the cylinder?

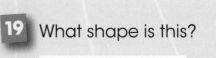

19 What shape is this?

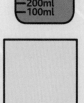

20 What number does the tally show?

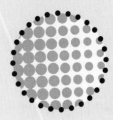

Score:

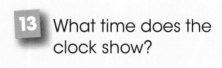

1 What is the sum of 8 and 5?

2 40 + 30 =

3 What number is 10 less than 76?

4 140 − 60 =

5 8 x 5 =

6 5 multiplied by 2 =

7 Divide 30 by 5.

8 45 ÷ 5 =

9 Count in hundreds: 300, 400, 500, 600... What number comes next?

10 Write these numbers in order (smallest first): 427 472 74

11 What fraction is shaded?

12 Colour nine tenths of the circle.

13 What time does the clock show?

14 There are _____ hours in one day.

15 3 metres = _____ centimetres

16 2kg = _____ grams

17 How much money altogether?

18 How much liquid in the cylinder?

19 What shape is this?

20 What number does the tally show?

卌 卌 卌

Digit says...

April, June, September and November are not my favourite months because I only get 30 walks in each of them.

Score:

Brodie's Brain Booster

I think of a number and add 7 to make 10. What number did I first think of?

1 What is the sum of 9 and 7?

2 50 + 40 =

3 What number is 10 less than 69?

4 120 – 70 =

5 4 x 5 =

6 5 multiplied by 8 =

7 Divide 25 by 5.

8 50 ÷ 5 =

9 Count in hundreds: 200, 300, 400, 500… What number comes next?

10 Write these numbers in order (smallest first): 89 988 889

11 What fraction is shaded?

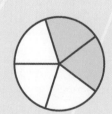

12 Colour one eighth of the circle.

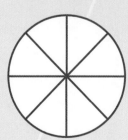

13 What time does the clock show?

14 There are _____ minutes in one hour.

15 4 metres = _____ centimetres

16 How many grams are there in three kilograms?

17 How much money altogether?

18 How much liquid in the cylinder?

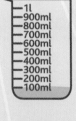

19 What shape is this?

20 What number does the tally show?

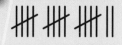

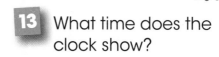

1 What is the sum of 6 and 5?

2 40 + 50 =

3 What number is 10 less than 99?

4 140 – 90 =

5 9 x 5 =

6 5 multiplied by 7 =

7 Divide 35 by 5.

8 60 ÷ 5 =

9 Count in hundreds: 600, 700, 800, 900... What number comes next?

10 Write these numbers in order, (smallest first): 923 932 39

11 What fraction is shaded?

12 Colour two eighths of the circle.

13 What time does the clock show?

14 There are   minutes in half an hour.

15 5 metres =   centimetres

16 3000g =   kg

17 How much money altogether?

18 How much liquid in the cylinder?

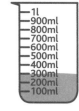

19 What shape is this?

20 What number does the tally show?

Digit says...

As well as January, I have 31 walks in March, May, July, August, October and December.

Addition

1 What is the sum of 7 and 8?

2 60 + 40 =

Subtraction

3 What number is 10 less than 100?

4 150 − 80 =

Multiplication

5 7 x 5 =

6 5 multiplied by 5 =

Division

7 Divide 45 by 5.

8 40 ÷ 5 =

Number and place value

9 Count in hundreds: 400, 500, 600, 700… What number comes next?

10 Write these numbers in order (smallest first): 718 187 87

Fractions

11 What fraction is shaded?

12 Colour three eighths of the circle.

Measures

13 What time does the clock show?

14 1 day =   hours

15 6 metres =   centimetres

16 3kg =   g

17 How much money altogether?

16 How much liquid in the cylinder?

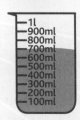

Geometry

19 What shape is this?

Data

20 What number does the tally show?

Test	6	7	8	9	10	Progress
Score						

14

TEST 11

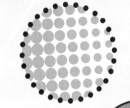

1 What is the total of 12 and 8?

2 345 + 9 =

3 What is the difference between 30 and 8?

4 20 – _____ = 5

5 7 x 4 =

6 Multiply 4 by 2.

7 32 ÷ 4 =

8 Share 16 between 4.

9 Count in fours: 0, 4, 8, 12… What number comes next?

10 Write these numbers in order (smallest first): 246 642 462

11 What fraction is shaded?

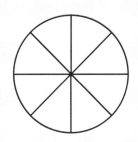

12 Colour three eighths of the circle.

13 What time does the clock show?

14 How many seconds are there in one minute?

15 How many centimetres are there in two metres?

16 How many grams are there in half a kilogram?

17 How much money altogether?

18 How much liquid in the cylinder?

19 What shape is this?

20 What number does the tally show?

卌 ||||

Brodie's Brain Booster

I think of a number and subtract 6 to make 16. What number did I first think of?

15

TEST 12

1 What is the total of 17 and 7?

2 562 + 8 =

3 What is the difference between 40 and 6?

4 20 − [ ] = 6

5 2 x 4 =

6 Multiply 4 by 8.

7 44 ÷ 4 =

8 Share 40 between 4.

9 Count in fours: 12, 16, 20, 24…
What number comes next?

10 Write these numbers in order
(smallest first): 819 918 891

11 What fraction
is shaded?

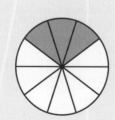

12 Colour one
eighth
of the circle.

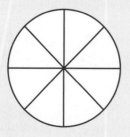

13 What time does the
clock show?

14 1 minute = [ ] seconds

15 How many centimetres are there
in three metres?

16 ½ kg = [ ] g

17 How much money
altogether?

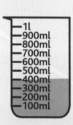

18 How much liquid
in the cylinder?

─1l
─900ml
─800ml
─700ml
─600ml
─500ml
─400ml
─300ml
─200ml
─100ml

19 What shape is this?

20 What number does the tally show?

IIII IIIII II

Digit says...

I have 365 walks in a
year and 366 walks in
a leap year. That's a
lot of walking!

16

Score:

Brodie's Brain Booster

I think of a number and multiply by 5 to make 15. What number did I first think of?

1 What is the total of 19 and 5?

2 $628 + 7 =$

3 What is the difference between 50 and 2?

4 $20 - = 7$

5 $3 \times 4 =$

6 Multiply 4 by 9.

7 $28 \div 4 =$

8 Share 24 between 4.

9 Count in fours: 8, 12, 16, 20…
What number comes next?

10 Write these numbers in order (smallest first): 472 274 724

11 What fraction is shaded?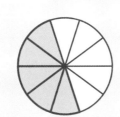

12 Colour four eighths of the circle.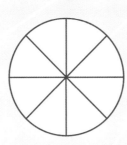

13 What time does the clock show?

14 $\frac{1}{2}$ minute = seconds

15 How many centimetres are there in four metres?

16 $500g = $ kg

17 How much money altogether?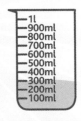

18 How much liquid in the cylinder?

19 What shape is this?

20 What number does the tally show?

17

TEST 14

Score:

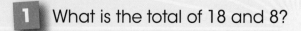

Digit says...

I have 3 dog biscuits every day (yummy!). That means I have 21 in a week.

1 What is the total of 18 and 8?

2 419 + 6 =

3 What is the difference between 20 and 7?

4 20 – ___ = 8

5 4 x 4 =

6 Multiply 4 by 12.

7 48 ÷ 4 =

8 Share 12 between 4.

9 Count in fours: 16, 20, 24, 28… What number comes next?

10 Write these numbers in order (smallest first): 536 635 563

11 What fraction is shaded?

12 Colour five eighths of the circle.

13 What time does the clock show?

14 How many minutes are there in one hour?

15 How many centimetres are there in five metres?

16 How many grams are there in half a kilogram?

17 How much money altogether?

18 How much liquid in the cylinder?

19 What shape is this?

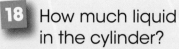

20 What number does the tally show?

|||| |||| ||||

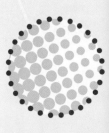

1 What is the total of 16 and 9?

2 786 + 9 =

3 What is the difference between 50 and 9?

4 20 – ____ = 9

5 5 x 4 =

6 Multiply 4 by 7.

7 36 ÷ 4 =

8 Share 48 between 4.

9 Count in fours: 24, 28, 32, 36… What number comes next?

10 Write these numbers in order (smallest first): 814 184 841

11 What fraction is shaded?

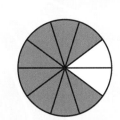

12 Colour six eighths of the circle.

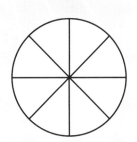

13 What time does the clock show?

14 1 hour = ____ minutes

15 How many centimetres are there in half a metre?

16 $\frac{1}{2}$ kg = ____ g

17 How much money altogether?

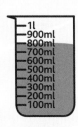
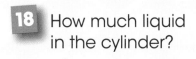

18 How much liquid in the cylinder?

19 What shape is this?

20 What number does the tally show?

𝍷𝍷𝍷𝍷 𝍷𝍷𝍷𝍷 𝍷𝍷𝍷

Brodie's Brain Booster

How many days are there in one year, when it isn't a leap year?

19

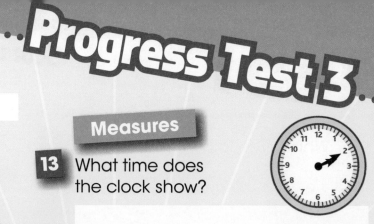

Addition

1 What is the sum of 19 and 9?

2 856 + 8 =

Subtraction

3 What is the difference between 60 and 4?

4 20 – _____ = 10

Multiplication

5 6 x 4 =

6 Multiply 4 by 8 =

Division

7 40 ÷ 4 =

8 Share 36 between 4.

Number and place value

9 Count in fours: 32, 36, 40, 44…
What number comes next?

10 Write these numbers in order
(smallest first): 322 223 232

Fractions

11 What fraction is shaded?

12 Colour seven eighths of the circle.

Measures

13 What time does the clock show?

14 $\frac{1}{2}$ hour = _____ minutes

15 How many centimetres are there in four metres?

16 500g = _____ kg

17 How much money altogether?

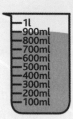

16 How much liquid in the cylinder?

Geometry

19 What shape is this?

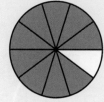

Data

20 What number does the tally show?

HHT HHT II

Score chart

Test	11	12	13	14	15	Progress
Score						

Score:

1 Add 12p to 20p.

2 217 + 60 =

3 30 subtract 9 =

4 369 – 8 =

5 9 x 3 =

6 Multiply 3 by 7.

7 21 ÷ 3 =

8 Half of 30 =

9 Count in eights: 0, 8, 16, 24…
What number comes next?

10 Write these numbers in order
(smallest first): 29 921 219 192

11 What fraction
is shaded?

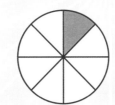

12 Colour one sixth
of the circle.

13 What time does the
clock show?

14 How many days
are there in one week?

15 How many centimetres
are there in two metres?

16 How many grams are
there in three kilograms?

17 How much money
altogether?

18 1l – 400ml =   ml

19 How many sides does a
square have?

20 What number does the tally show?

卌 卌 卌 ||

Digit says...

Remember that am means
the morning. I've trained my
humans to put dog food in my
bowl at 7am every morning.

Score:

1 Add 15p to 20p.

2 319 + 50 =

3 40 subtract 9 =

4 487 – 6 =

5 4 x 3 =

6 Multiply 3 by 8.

7 15 ÷ 3 =

8 Half of 20 =

9 Count in eights: 8, 16, 24, 32…
What number comes next?

10 Write these numbers in order
(smallest first): 514 54 145 541

11 What fraction
is shaded?

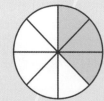

12 Colour two
sixths of
the circle.

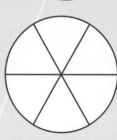

13 What time does the
clock show?

14 1 week =   days

15 How many centimetres are there
in one and a half metres?

16 4 kilograms =   grams

17 How much money
altogether?

18 1l - 500ml =   ml

19 How many sides does a
triangle have?

20 What number does the tally show?

|||| |||| ||||

Brodie's Brain Booster

How many days are there in a leap year?

TEST 18

1 Add 17p to 20p.

2 423 + 70 =

3 50 subtract 9 =

4 999 – 8 =

5 7 x 3 =

6 Multiply 3 by 9.

7 12 ÷ 3 =

8 Half of 40 =

9 Count in eights: 16, 24, 32, 40…
What number comes next?

10 Write these numbers in order
(smallest first): 623 326 632 362

11 What fraction
is shaded?

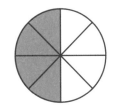

12 Colour three
sixths of
the circle.

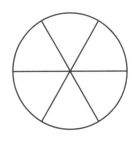

13 What time does the
clock show?

14 2 weeks =   days

15 How many centimetres are there in
two and a half metres?

16 4000 grams =   kilograms

17 How much money
altogether?

18 1l – 800ml =   ml

19 How many sides does a
rectangle have?

20 What number does the tally show?

Digit says...

Remember that pm means
the afternoon and evening.
I've trained my humans to
give me more food at 5pm.

TEST 19

Score:

Four people share some sweets so that they have 5 sweets each. How many sweets did they share out?

1 Add 18p to 20p.

2 518 + 40 =

3 60 subtract 9 =

4 718 – 6 =

5 8 x 3 =

6 Multiply 3 by 6.

7 27 ÷ 3 =

8 Half of 50 =

9 Count in eights: 24, 32, 40, 48… What number comes next?

10 Write these numbers in order (smallest first): 769 967 976 796

11 What fraction is shaded?

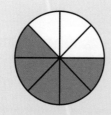

12 Colour four sixths of the circle.

13 What time does the clock show?

14 3 weeks = _____ days

15 How many centimetres are there in three and a half metres?

16 2kg = _____ g

17 How much money altogether?

18 1l – 600ml = _____ ml

19 How many sides does a hexagon have?

20 What number does the tally show?

‖‖‖ ‖‖‖ ‖‖‖ ‖‖‖ |||

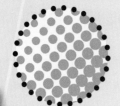

TEST 20

1 Add 19p to 20p.

2 624 + 70 =

3 70 subtract 9 =

4 555 – 4 =

5 6 x 3 =

6 Multiply 3 by 5.

7 24 ÷ 3 =

8 Half of 60 =

9 Count in eights: 32, 40, 48, 56…
What number comes next?

10 Write these numbers in order
(smallest first): 458 548 485 584

11 What fraction
is shaded?

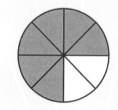

12 Colour five
sixths of
the circle.

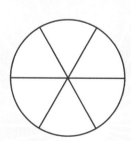

13 What time does the
clock show?

14 4 weeks =   days

15 $1\frac{1}{2}$ metres =   centimetres

16 3000g =   kg

17 How much money
altogether?

18 1l – 900ml =   ml

19 How many sides does a
pentagon have?

20 What number does the tally show?

|||| |||| |||| ||||

Digit says...

I have two bowls of
dog food every single
day. That means that
some months I get 62
bowls of dog food!

Addition

1 Add 13p to 20p.

2 $716 + 80 =$

Subtraction

3 80 subtract 9 =

4 $827 - 5 =$

Multiplication

5 $5 \times 3 =$

6 Multiply 3 by 12.

Division

7 $33 \div 3 =$

8 Half of 70 =

Number and place value

9 Count in eights: 48, 56, 64, 72…
What number comes next?

10 Write these numbers in order
(smallest first): 825 528 852 582

Fractions

11 What fraction
is shaded?

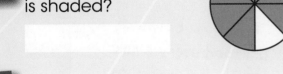

12 Colour two thirds
of the circle.

Measures

13 What time does
the clock show?

14 5 weeks =   days

15 $2\frac{1}{2}$ metres =   centimetres

16 4kg =   g

17 How much
money altogether?

16 1l – 700ml =   ml

Geometry

19 How many sides does a hexagon
have?

Data

20 What number does the tally show?

卌 卌 卌 卌 ||

Score chart

Test	16	17	18	19	20	Progress
Score						

26

Score:

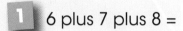

1 6 plus 7 plus 8 =

2 87 + 22 =

3 45 take away 6 =

4 487 – 30 =

5 4 x 8 =

6 Multiply 8 by 3.

7 72 ÷ 8 =

8 Divide 40 by 8.

9 Count in fifties: 0, 50, 100, 150…
What number comes next?

10 Write < or >. 7   9

11 What fraction is shaded?

12 Colour half of the circles.

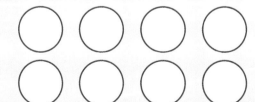

13 Draw hands on the clock face to show 5 o'clock.

14 $\frac{1}{2}$ hour =   minutes

15 1m =   cm

16 How many millilitres are there in one litre?

17 How much money altogether?

18 1l – 300ml =   ml

19 How many sides does a square have?

20 What number does the tally show?

Brodie's Brain Booster

In which months does Digit the dog have 62 bowls of dog food?

TEST 22

Score:

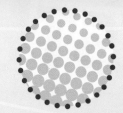

1 5 plus 9 plus 4 =

2 56 + 23 =

3 45 take away 7 =

4 592 – 60 =

5 3 x 8 =

6 Multiply 8 by 12.

7 32 ÷ 8 =

8 Divide 64 by 8.

9 Count in fifties: 100, 150, 200, 250…
What number comes next?

10 Write < or >. 12   9

11 What fraction is shaded?

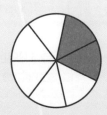

12 Colour half of the pentagons.

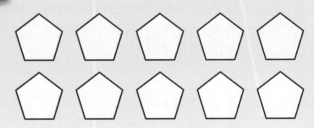

13 Draw hands on the clock face to show a half past 2.

14 1 hour =   minutes

15 2m =   cm

16 1 litre =   millilitres

17 How much money altogether?

18 1l – 600ml =   ml

19 How many sides does a triangle have?

20 What number does the tally show?

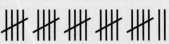

Digit says…

My dog bowl has 8 sides so it's octagonal.

TEST 23

Score:

Brodie's Brain Booster

In which months does Digit the dog have 60 bowls of dog food?

1 8 plus 3 plus 2 =

2 72 + 25 =

3 45 take away 8 =

4 858 – 40 =

5 9 x 8 =

6 Multiply 8 by 4.

7 24 ÷ 8 =

8 Divide 48 by 8.

9 Count in fifties: 250, 300, 350, 400…
What number comes next?

13 Draw hands on the clock face to show a quarter past 1.

14 1 minute =   seconds

15 3m =   cm

16 1000 millilitres =   litre

17 How much money altogether?

10 Write < or >. 5   11

11 What fraction is shaded?

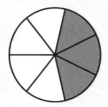

12 Colour half of the squares.

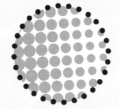

18 1l – 100ml =   ml

19 How many sides does a rectangle have?

20 What number does the tally show?

|||| |||| |||| |||| |||| ||||

29

Score:

Digit says...

My water bowl is circular so it has no corners.

1 7 plus 8 plus 9 =

2 63 + 34 =

3 45 take away 9 =

4 976 – 50 =

5 5 x 8 =

6 Multiply 8 by 6.

7 64 ÷ 8 =

8 Divide 56 by 8.

9 Count in fifties: 450, 500, 550, 600…
What number comes next?

10 Write < or >. 17 ___ 13

11 What fraction is shaded?

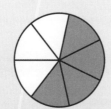

12 Colour half of the hexagons.

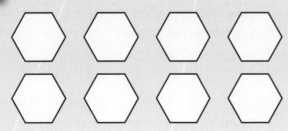

13 Draw hands on the clock face to show a quarter to 4.

14 $\frac{1}{2}$ minute = ___ seconds

15 3m = ___ cm

16 How many millilitres are there in one litre?

17 How much money altogether?

18 1l – 800ml = ___ ml

19 How many sides does an octagon have?

20 What number does the tally show?

Score:

1 8 plus 0 plus 7 =

2 45 + 24 =

3 53 take away 6 =

4 368 – 40 =

5 6 x 8 =

6 Multiply 8 by 7.

7 48 ÷ 8 =

8 Divide 96 by 8.

9 Count in fifties: 600, 650, 700, 750…
What number comes next?

10 Write < or >. 19   24

11 What fraction is shaded?

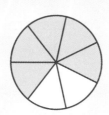

12 Colour half of the stars.

13 Draw hands on the clock face to show 5 past 3.

14 1 week =   days

15 4m =   cm

16 1 litre =   millilitres

17 How much money altogether?

18 1l – 700ml =   ml

19 How many sides does a pentagon have?

20 What number does the tally show?

||||| ||||| ||||| ||||| |||||

Brodie's Brain Booster

In which month does Digit the dog usually just have 56 bowls of dog food?

31

Addition

1 4 plus 8 plus 9 =

2 86 + 17 =

Subtraction

3 53 take away 7 =

4 684 – 50 =

Multiplication

5 7 x 8 =

6 Multiply 8 by 5.

Division

7 96 ÷ 8 =

8 Divide 88 by 8.

Number and place value

9 Count in fifties: 500, 550, 600, 650…
What number comes next?

10 Write < or >. 22   18

Fractions

11 What fraction is shaded?

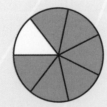

12 Colour half of the octagons

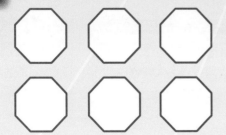

Measures

13 Draw hands on the clock face to show 10 past 10.

14 2 weeks =   days

15 5m =   cm

16 1000 millilitres =   litre

17 How much money altogether?

16 1l – 900ml =   ml

Geometry

19 How many sides does an octagon have?

Data

20 What number does the tally show?

▤ ▤ ▤ ▤ ▤

32

Score:

Digit says…

Did you know that the corners of shapes can also be called vertices. Cats don't know that but I do!

1 What number is 100 more than 243?

2 4 + ___ = 20

3 What is my change from 50p if I spend 32p?

4 962 – 300 =

5 4 x 100 =

6 Double 14 =

7 24 ÷ ___ = 4

8 80 ÷ 10 =

9 Count down in tens: 100, 90, 80, 70… What number comes next?

10 Write < or >. 13 ___ 31

11 What fraction is shaded?

12 Colour one quarter of the circles.

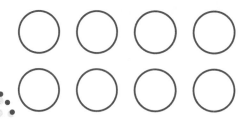

13 Draw hands on the clock face to show 20 past 6.

14 How many minutes are there in one hour?

15 100cm = ___ m

16 How many millilitres are there in two litres?

17 How much money altogether?

18 400ml + ___ ml = 1l

19 How many vertices does a square have?

20 What number does the tally show?

|||| |||| |||| |||| |||| |||| ||

Score:

1 What number is 100 more than 519?

2 5 + ☐ = 20

3 What is my change from 50p if I spend 27p?

4 815 − 400 =

5 2 × 100 =

6 Double 12 =

7 32 ÷ ☐ = 4

8 60 ÷ 10 =

9 Count down in tens: 60, 50, 40, 30... What number comes next?

10 Write < or >. 48 ☐ 37

11 What fraction is shaded?

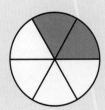

12 Colour one quarter of the circles.

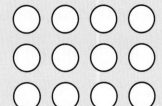

13 Draw hands on the clock face to show 25 past 2.

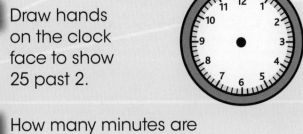

14 How many minutes are there in half an hour?

15 200cm = ☐ m

16 2 litres = ☐ millilitres

17 How much money altogether?

18 500ml + ☐ ml = 1l

19 How many vertices does a triangle have?

20 What number does the tally show?

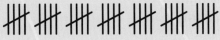

Brodie's Brain Booster

One bag of Digit's dog food costs £13. How much would 2 bags of dog food cost?

TEST 28

Score:

Digit says...

Sometimes I go west for my walk and sometimes I go in the opposite direction, which is east.

1 What number is 100 more than 682?

2 6 +   = 20

3 What is my change from 50p if I spend 14p?

4 748 − 200 =

5 6 x 100 =

6 Double 11 =

7 40 ÷   = 4

8 90 ÷ 10 =

9 Count down in tens: 90, 80, 70, 60… What number comes next?

10 Write < or >. 19   91

11 What fraction is shaded?

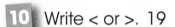

12 Colour one quarter of the circles.

13 Draw hands on the clock face to show 25 to 9.

14 How many minutes are there in a quarter of an hour?

15 300cm =   m

16 5000 millilitres =   litres

17 How much money altogether?

18 400ml +   ml = 1l

19 How many vertices does a rectangle have?

20 What number does the tally show?

||||| ||||| ||||| ||||| ||||| ||||| ||||| ||||

35

Score:

Brodie's Brain Booster

One bag of Digit's dog food costs £13. If I buy one bag for him, how much change will I get from £20?

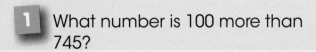

1 What number is 100 more than 745?

2 7 + ___ = 20

3 What is my change from 50p if I spend 39p?

4 654 − 300 =

5 8 x 100 =

6 Double 13 =

7 20 ÷ ___ = 4

8 40 ÷ 10 =

9 Count down in tens: 120, 110, 100, 90... What number comes next?

10 Write < or >. 25 ___ 52

11 What fraction is shaded?

12 Colour one quarter of the circles.

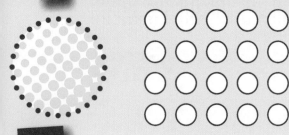

13 Draw hands on the clock face to show 20 to 1.

14 How many seconds are there in one minute?

15 400cm = ___ m

16 How many millilitres are there in three litres?

17 How much money altogether?

18 100ml + ___ ml = 1l

19 How many vertices does an octagon have?

20 What number does the tally show?

Score:

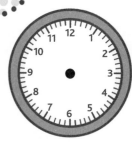

1 What number is 100 more than 889?

2 8 + ___ = 20

3 What is my change from 50p if I spend 22p?

4 729 – 500 =

5 7 x 100 =

6 Double 15 =

7 36 ÷ ___ = 4

8 30 ÷ 10 =

9 Count down in tens: 80, 70, 60, 50… What number comes next?

10 Write < or >. 35 ___ 53

11 What fraction is shaded?

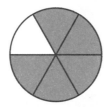

12 Colour one quarter of the circles.

13 Draw hands on the clock face to show 10 to 12.

14 How many seconds are there in half a minute?

15 500cm = ___ m

16 3 litres = ___ millilitres

17 How much money altogether?

18 300ml + ___ ml = 1l

19 How many vertices does a pentagon have?

20 What number does the tally show?

卌 卌 卌 卌 卌 卌 ||||

Digit says...

My ball used to be a perfect sphere but somebody bit a hole in it. I blame the cat!

Addition

1 What number is 100 more than 476?

2 $9 + \boxed{} = 20$

Subtraction

3 What is my change from 50p if I spend 38p?

4 $859 - 600 = \boxed{}$

Multiplication

5 $9 \times 100 = \boxed{}$

6 Double 16 =

Division

7 $28 \div \boxed{} = 4$

8 $70 \div 10 = \boxed{}$

Number and place value

9 Count down in tens: 140, 130, 120, 110… What number comes next?

10 Write < or >. 87 $\boxed{}$ 78

Fractions

11 What fraction is shaded?

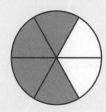

12 Colour one quarter of the circles.

Measures

13 Draw hands on the clock face to show 5 to 5.

14 How many seconds are there in a quarter of a minute?

15 300cm = $\boxed{}$ m

16 2000 millilitres = $\boxed{}$ litres

17 How much money altogether?

16 700ml + $\boxed{}$ = 1l

Geometry

19 How many vertices does an octagon have?

Data

20 What number does the tally show?

卌 卌 卌 卌 卌 卌 卌 |||

Score chart

Test	26	27	28	29	30	Progress
Score						

38

Score:

Brodie's Brain Booster

I have 62 stamps in my collection. How many will I have if I give half my collection to my sister?

1 492 + 200 =

2 What number is 100 less than 732?

3 100 – 62 =

4 What is my change from £1 if I spend 76p?

5 17 x 10 =

6 40 x 3 =

7   x 8 = 48

8 700 divided by 10 =

9 Count down in hundreds:
800, 700, 600, 500…
What number comes next?

10 Write < or >. 148   184

11 What fraction is shaded?

12 Colour three quarters of the circles.

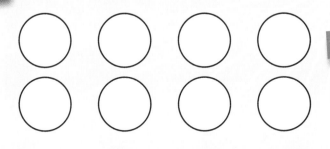

13 Draw hands on the clock face to show 20 past 6.

14 How many seconds are there in a quarter of a minute?

15 100cm =   m

16 How many millilitres are there in three litres?

17 How much money altogether?

18 40cm +   = 1m

19 How many vertices does a square have?

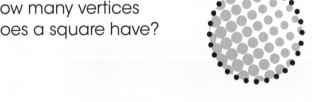

20 What number does the tally show?

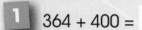

TEST 32 Score:

1 364 + 400 =

2 What number is 100 less than 417?

3 100 – 36 =

4 What is my change from £1 if I spend 27p?

5 28 x 10 =

6 20 x 3 =

7 _____ x 8 = 64

8 300 divided by 10 =

9 Count down in hundreds: 600, 500, 400, 300… What number comes next?

10 Write < or >. 623 _____ 326

11 What fraction is shaded?

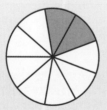

12 Colour three quarters of the squares.

13 Draw hands on the clock face to show 25 past 6.

14 How many seconds are there in half a minute?

15 1m = _____ cm

16 3 litres = _____ millilitres

17 How much money altogether?

18 10cm + _____ = 1m

19 How many vertices does a triangle have?

20 What number does the tally show?

卌 卌 卌 卌 卌 卌 卌 卌 卌

Digit says...

My humans say I'm more expensive to keep than the cat but I think I'm worth it!

Score:

Brodie's Brain Booster

One bag of Digit's dog food costs £13. He needs 3 bags each week. How much do I spend on his dog food each week?

1 215 + 500 =

2 What number is 100 less than 132?

3 100 – 47 =

4 What is my change from £1 if I spend 19p?

5 43 x 10 =

6 50 x 3 =

7   x 8 = 88

8 900 divided by 10 =

9 Count down in hundreds:
1000, 900, 800, 700…
What number comes next?

10 Write < or >. 297   279

11 What fraction is shaded?

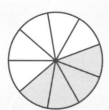

12 Colour three quarters of the triangles.

13 Draw hands on the clock face to show 25 to 7.

14 How many seconds are there in three quarters of a minute?

15 200cm =   m

16 3000 millilitres =   litres

17 How much money altogether?

18 90cm +   = 1m

19 How many vertices does a rectangle have?

20 What number does the tally show?

̶H̶H̶ ̶H̶H̶ ̶H̶H̶ ̶H̶H̶ ̶H̶H̶ ̶H̶H̶ ̶H̶H̶ ̶H̶H̶ |||

1   732 + 200 =

2   What number is 100 less than 827?

3   100 – 81 =

4   What is my change from £1 if I spend 58p?

5   17 x 10 =

6   20 x 3 =

7   x 8 = 72

8   600 divided by 10 =

9   Count down in hundreds:
400, 300, 200, 100…
What number comes next?

10   Write < or >.   312   321

11   What fraction is shaded?

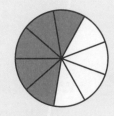

12   Colour three quarters of the pentagons.

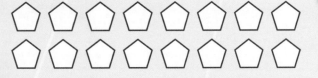

Digit says...

Did you know there are 1000 grams in a kilogram? I wonder how many grams of food I eat every day.

13   Draw hands on the clock face to show 20 to 7.

14   How many minutes are there in a quarter of an hour?

15   2m =   cm

16   4000ml =   l

17   How much money altogether?

18   80cm +   = 1m

19   How many vertices does an octagon have?

20   What number does the tally show?

Score:

1 655 + 300 =

2 What number is 100 less than 1000?

3 100 − 28 =

4 What is my change from £1 if I spend 62p?

5 19 x 10 =

6 40 x 3 =

7 _____ x 8 = 96

8 800 divided by 10 =

9 Count down in hundreds:
700, 600, 500, 400…
What number comes next?

10 Write < or >. 567 _____ 576

11 What fraction is shaded?

12 Colour three quarters of the hexagons.

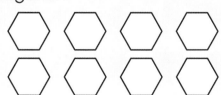

13 Draw hands on the clock face to show 10 to 7.

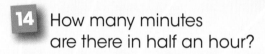

14 How many minutes are there in half an hour?

15 300cm = _____ m

16 2000ml = _____ l

17 How much money altogether?

18 30cm + _____ = 1m

19 How many vertices does a pentagon have?

20 What number does the tally show?

|||| |||| |||| |||| |||| |||| |||| |||| ||||||||

Brodie's Brain Booster

One bag of Digit's dog food costs £13. He needs 3 bags each week. How much do I spend on his dog food to buy enough for February?

43

Addition

1 587 + 200 =

2 What number is 100 less than 955?

Subtraction

3 100 − 55 =

4 What is my change from £1 if I spend 29p?

Multiplication

5 59 x 10 =

6 50 x 3 =

Division

7 ____ x 8 = 56

8 400 divided by 10 =

Number and place value

9 Count down in hundreds: 500, 400, 300, 200… What number comes next?

10 Write < or >. 834 ____ 843

Fractions

11 What fraction is shaded?

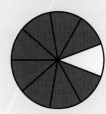

12 Colour three quarters of the octagons.

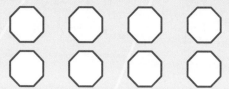

Measures

13 Draw hands on the clock face to show 5 to 7.

14 How many minutes are there in three quarter of an hour?

15 3m = ____ cm

16 ½l = ____ ml

17 How much money altogether?

18 70cm + ____ = 1m

Geometry

19 How many vertices does an octagon have?

Data

20 What number does the tally show?

𝍸𝍸 𝍸𝍸 𝍸𝍸 𝍸𝍸 𝍸𝍸 𝍸𝍸 𝍸𝍸 𝍸𝍸 𝍸𝍸 𝍸𝍸 ||

Score chart

Test	31	32	33	34	35	Progress
Score						

ANSWERS

	Test 1	Test 2	Test 3	Test 4	Test 5	Progress Test 1
1	37	58	71	103	46	95
2	17	13	14	12	15	13
3	14	16	27	9	13	11
4	73	81	86	48	54	81
5	18	12	16	8	14	22
6	14	16	14	10	8	16
7	4	10	9	8	7	12
8	10	6	12	7	12	9
9	40	70	60	90	80	100
10	78 87 97	23 32 43	56 59 65	25 35 52	17 71 77	29 92 99
11	$\frac{1}{2}$	$\frac{1}{4}$	$\frac{2}{4}$ or $\frac{1}{2}$	$\frac{3}{4}$	$\frac{1}{3}$	$\frac{2}{3}$
12	(pie chart)	(pie chart)	(pie chart)	(pie chart)	(pie chart)	(pie chart)
13	6 o'clock	half past 4	quarter past 1	quarter to 9	5 past 7	10 past 8
14	60	60	60	30	60	30
15	100	100	50	1	$\frac{1}{2}$	100
16	1000	1000	1	500	500	$\frac{1}{2}$
17	23p	53p	65p	56p	57p	35p
18	700ml	200ml	300ml	600ml	800ml	500ml
19	triangle	square	rectangle	hexagon	octagon	pentagon
20	7	6	8	9	10	11

	Test 6	Test 7	Test 8	Test 9	Test 10	Progress Test 2
1	17	11	13	16	11	15
2	80	80	70	90	90	100
3	74	83	66	59	89	90
4	50	130	80	50	50	70
5	30	15	40	20	45	35
6	45	30	10	40	35	25
7	8	4	6	5	7	9
8	5	7	9	10	12	8
9	400	500	700	600	1000	800
10	46 146 164	32 132 312	74 427 472	89 889 988	39 923 932	87 187 718
11	$\frac{1}{3}$	$\frac{2}{3}$	$\frac{1}{5}$	$\frac{2}{5}$	$\frac{3}{5}$	$\frac{4}{5}$
12	(pie chart)	(pie chart)	(pie chart)	(pie chart)	(pie chart)	(pie chart)
13	20 past 6	25 past 9	25 to 10	20 to 4	10 to 3	5 to 2
14	24	24	24	60	30	24
15	100	200	300	400	500	600
16	2000	2	2000	3000	3	3000
17	35p	31p	32p	30p	27p	26p
18	800ml	600ml	500ml	100ml	300ml	700ml
19	triangle	square	rectangle	hexagon	octagon	octagon
20	14	12	15	17	10	11

	Test 11	Test 12	Test 13	Test 14	Test 15	Progress Test 3
1	20	24	24	26	25	28
2	354	570	635	425	795	864
3	22	34	48	13	41	56
4	15	14	13	12	11	10
5	28	8	12	16	20	24
6	8	32	36	48	28	32
7	8	11	7	12	9	10
8	4	10	6	3	12	9
9	16	28	24	32	40	52
10	246 462 642	819 891 918	274 472 724	536 563 635	184 814 841	223 232 322
11	$\frac{1}{10}$	$\frac{3}{10}$	$\frac{5}{10}$ or $\frac{1}{2}$	$\frac{7}{10}$	$\frac{8}{10}$ or $\frac{4}{5}$	$\frac{9}{10}$
12						
13	11 o'clock	half past 12	quarter past 1	quarter to 8	5 past 4	10 past 2
14	60	60	30	60	60	30
15	200	300	400	500	50	400
16	500	500	$\frac{1}{2}$	500	500	$\frac{1}{2}$
17	56p	57p	60p	54p	52p	53p
18	600ml	400ml	300ml	700ml	800ml	900ml
19	triangle	square	rectangle	hexagon	octagon	pentagon
20	9	12	11	15	13	12

	Test 16	Test 17	Test 18	Test 19	Test 20	Progress Test 4
1	32p	35p	37p	38p	39p	33p
2	277	369	493	558	694	796
3	21	31	41	51	61	71
4	361	481	991	712	551	822
5	27	12	21	24	18	15
6	21	24	27	18	15	36
7	7	5	4	9	8	11
8	15	10	20	25	30	35
9	32	40	48	56	64	80
10	29 192 219 921	54 145 514 541	326 362 623 632	769 796 967 976	458 485 548 584	528 582 825 852
11	$\frac{1}{8}$	$\frac{3}{8}$	$\frac{4}{8}$ or $\frac{1}{2}$	$\frac{5}{8}$	$\frac{6}{8}$ or $\frac{3}{4}$	$\frac{7}{8}$
12						
13	20 past 2	25 past 8	25 to 10	20 to 9	10 to 3	5 to 1
14	7	7	14	21	28	35
15	200	150	250	350	150	250
16	3000	4000	4	2000	3	4000
17	80p	90p	65p	75p	72p	71p
18	600ml	500ml	200ml	400ml	100ml	300
19	4	3	4	6	5	6
20	17	14	20	23	19	22

	Test 21	Test 22	Test 23	Test 24	Test 25	Progress Test 5
1	21	18	13	24	15	21
2	109	79	97	97	69	103
3	39	38	37	36	47	46
4	457	532	818	926	328	634
5	32	24	72	40	48	56
6	24	96	32	48	56	40
7	9	4	3	8	6	12
8	5	8	6	7	12	11
9	200	300	450	650	800	700
10	<	>	<	>	<	>
11	$\frac{1}{7}$	$\frac{2}{7}$	$\frac{3}{7}$	$\frac{4}{7}$	$\frac{5}{7}$	$\frac{6}{7}$
12	4 coloured	5 coloured	3 coloured	6 coloured	4 coloured	3 coloured
13						
14	30	60	60	30	7	14
15	100	200	300	300	400	500
16	1000	1000	1	1000	1000	1
17	75p	71p	80p	45p	72p	80p
18	700ml	400ml	900ml	200ml	300ml	100ml
19	4	3	4	8	5	8
20	23	27	29	28	26	25

	Test 26	Test 27	Test 28	Test 29	Test 30	Progress Test 6
1	343	619	782	845	989	576
2	16	15	14	13	12	11
3	18p	23p	36p	11p	28p	12p
4	662	415	548	354	229	259
5	400	200	600	800	700	900
6	28	24	22	26	30	32
7	6	8	10	5	9	7
8	8	6	9	4	3	7
9	60	20	50	80	40	100
10	<	>	<	<	<	>
11	$\frac{1}{6}$	$\frac{2}{6}$ or $\frac{1}{3}$	$\frac{3}{6}$ or $\frac{1}{2}$	$\frac{4}{6}$ or $\frac{2}{3}$	$\frac{5}{6}$	$\frac{4}{6}$ or $\frac{2}{3}$
12	2 coloured	3 coloured	4 coloured	5 coloured	6 coloured	2 coloured
13						
14	60	30	15	60	30	15
15	1	2	3	4	5	3
16	2000	2000	5	3000	3000	2
17	85p	75p	82p	81p	80p	74p
18	600	500	600	900	700	300
19	4	3	4	8	5	8
20	32	35	39	37	34	38

	Test 31	Test 32	Test 33	Test 34	Test 35	Progress Test 7
1	692	764	715	932	955	787
2	632	317	32	727	900	855
3	38	64	53	19	72	45
4	24p	73p	81p	42p	38p	71p
5	170	280	430	170	190	590
6	120	60	150	60	120	150
7	6	8	11	9	12	7
8	70	30	90	60	80	40
9	400	200	600	0	300	100
10	<	>	>	<	<	<
11	$\frac{1}{9}$	$\frac{2}{9}$	$\frac{4}{9}$	$\frac{5}{9}$	$\frac{7}{9}$	$\frac{8}{9}$
12	6 coloured	9 coloured	6 coloured	12 coloured	6 coloured	6 coloured
13	(clock)	(clock)	(clock)	(clock)	(clock)	(clock)
14	15	30	45	15	30	45
15	1	100	2	200	3	300
16	3000	3000	3	4	2	500
17	55p	46p	50p	52p	44p	42p
18	60cm	90cm	10cm	20cm	70cm	30cm
19	4	3	4	8	5	8
20	41	45	43	46	49	47

Brodie's Brain Booster

Test 1	57p
Test 3	57
Test 5	24
Test 7	80
Test 9	3
Test 11	22
Test 13	3
Test 15	365
Test 17	366
Test 19	20
Test 21	January, March, May, July, August, October, December
Test 23	April, June, September, November
Test 25	February
Test 27	£26
Test 29	£7
Test 31	31
Test 33	£39
Test 35	£156

Digit says...

"Well done and see you next time"